May I Go Out?

Written by Erin Rosenberg

Illustrated by Marilyn Mets

MODERN CURRICULUM PRESS

Program Consultants

Becky Dugan, *Teacher*
Brady Elementary School
Little Rock, Arkansas

Judy Stobbe, *Bilingual Teacher*
Alianza School
Watsonville, California

Debra List, *Teacher*
Hansberry ChildParent Center-
Chicago, Illinois

Wanda Tansil, *Teacher*
University Terrace School
Baton Rouge, Louisiana

Executive Editor: Dorrie Berkowitz

Associate Editor: Marcia Formichelli

Design concept: Paula Radding/BILL SMITH STUDIO

MODERN CURRICULUM PRESS
An imprint of Paramount Supplemental Education
250 James Street
Morristown, New Jersey 07960

ISBN: 0-8136-7973-7 (single copy)   0-8136-7974-5 (6-pack)

2 3 4 5 6 7 8 9 DP 99 98 97 96 95

 "Please, Teacher, may I go out?"

 "Where are your boots?"

 "They are with my coat."

"Where should they be?"

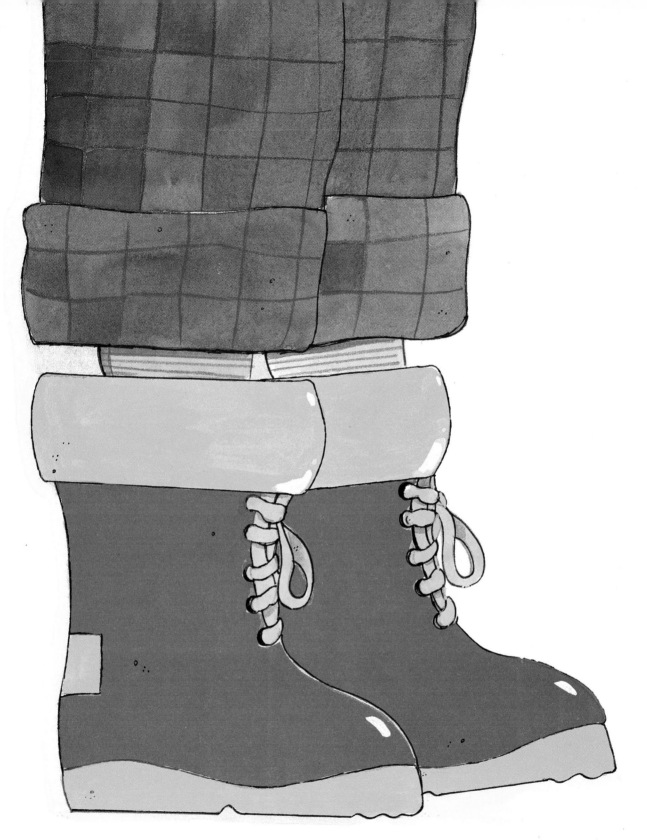

 "They should be on my feet!"

 "Where is your hat?"

 "It is with my coat."

 "Where should it be?"

 "It should be on my head!"

 "Where is your scarf?"

 "It is with my coat."

 "Where should it be?"

 "It should be around my neck!"

 "Where are your mittens?"

 "They are with my coat."

 "Where should they be?"

11

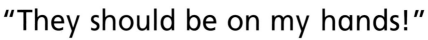 "They should be on my hands!"

"Please may I go out now?"

 "Sure you may!
But where is your coat?"